COMING HOME

Melea J. Brock
Right-Side-Up Stories
260 South Lake Avenue, PMB 185
Pasadena, CA 91101

All stories in this book have been
published previously in other form.

Scripture quotation in this publication is from
Spirit Filled Life® Bible
Copyright ©1991 by Thomas Nelson

Library of Congress
Card Catalogue Number: 00-109378
ISBN 0-9667455-1-5

COMING HOME

Volume II

in the

Right-Side-Up

Stories Series

Written by

Melea J. Brock

Edited by Marcia Coppess

Design & Illustration by Karen Newe

Published by Right-Side-Up Stories
Pasadena, CA

A story
is a friendly
visitor.

It knocks gently on the door
of our heart.
We readily let it in the
front door with an,
"Oh, it's you! Come on in!"
Story takes the best seat
in our home.
And pretty soon it's
telling us things
about our life and the
way we live that we
hadn't quite expected from
such a simple guest.

And so I dedicate this book
to all those who
let story in the door
of their hearts.
You won't be disappointed
by this
friendly visitor.

Contents

HOME CAN BE ONE OF THE MOST WONDERFUL places imaginable. And home has always been very important for me. Even though—or perhaps because—I didn't come from the best of homes, I've searched for it, longed for it and written stories about it. Through my Heavenly Father, countless dear friends, my husband and children and my two sisters, I have found the place called home deep inside of me.

Turn a page or two and you'll read this author's hopes in prose. It's called *The Place Called "Home"* (pages 5-8). As you read through the stories in this collection would you use this piece as a lens of discovery? Would you read with the word 'home' in mind and hear its call to you today?

For most of us, the call of home means our immediate family. But we can always place more leaves in the dining room table and include others outside those boundaries. I feel a great sense of family with people that I'll never be related to by blood. As I have traveled as a storyteller, I have been at home while sitting around a stranger's table as well as in churches, schools and huge gatherings. That's because we all carry the place called home inside of us. Down deep, God the Father has placed a yearning in us for Him—Our True Home. And He says in His Word that He and His Son Jesus will come and set up home in us:

> If anyone loves Me he will keep my word; and my Father will love him, and We will come to him and make Our home with him. *John 14:23*

I've written these stories for the church, the family, the neighborhood—those far away and those close to home. And I've written them with all ears in mind—child through adult. As with my first book of stories, these stories are meant to be read aloud as well! They've always been shared this way. Share these stories—out loud— in that wonderful living room voice you possess. Share them in your Sunday school classes, women's, men's and youth gatherings. Share them in schools and places of work and business. Share these stories in your living rooms, at dining room tables and by the sides of beds. Share them in unexpected places such as hospital rooms, waiting rooms, board rooms. Share them on long car rides, over tea and coffee with the unexpected stranger or guest. Share them!

If you're a pastor or worship leader, raise these stories in worship and use them as sermon illustrations. I have taken every story in this collection to more than 15 denominations. I know they will reach your church family's heart. My prayer is that one of these stories will bring hope, healing and understanding to your church family.

If you would like to use a story in a public performance for a school, church or community gathering, please seek my permission first. I also ask that you make mention of my authorship, make no copies or recordings of my story and lead people back to my storytelling ministry so that I may share my work with them as well (see *About Melea J. Brock and Right-Side-Up Stories* page 86).

Thanks for taking the time to read these stories and share them with others. I'm honored.

Enjoy!

Melea

The Place Called Home

*There is a place
called home for all of us.
It's not far away—and
closer than you would
dare to believe.*

*T*HERE IS A PLACE CALLED HOME FOR ALL OF US. It's not far away—and closer than you would dare to believe. For some of us, it takes years to find home. Some of us run away from it. Some of us stumble upon home quite by accident. Sometimes, we mistake home for a place that seems to possess a sense of hominess. But after awhile, we realize this just doesn't feel like home.

Some of us are born right into home, and some of us have the rare privilege of bringing it to others. Some of us are far away from home. We've never had home. We are orphans, if you will. How will we find what we've never had? And still, there are others.

Some us just rent home, if you know what I mean. Maybe we think we can't afford this place, or maybe we're afraid of that final kind of permanence home represents. One thing I know for certain: There is a place called home for all of us. And home is one of the most wonderful places imaginable.

You can put your feet on the coffee tables at home. You can leave your socks on the floor at home. You can move the furniture around as many times as you like. Or you can pack the whole thing up, move it somewhere else and call that new place your "new home." The menu is always good there, whether it's franks and beans or turkey with all the trimmings. The conversation is long and satisfying. Everyone gets a chance to speak his or her mind.

Oh, sure, there are disagreements at home. The voices might even rise to a fevered pitch. But at home one tries hard to hear what the other person is saying. And with hands locked tight, face to face, we agree to try to understand.

One finds forgiveness there over and over and over again. And if you have been hurt or wounded to the very deepest part, run fast to home. They'll be waiting. They'll take the time to listen and they'll pass the tissues as many times as needed.

Then there's the laughter at home. Plenty of it at home. From playful giggles to red-faced sore-tummied hilarity. It's true you can be yourself there. It's such a comfort to know you don't have to be anyone else except yourself. You can dare to be average—even regular—at home. Ah, but you can show off there, too, because they're easily impressed at home.

The welcome mat is wide and long there. One can bring home the dog, the cat and the bird with the broken wing. The stranger will be accepted with the same amount of enthusiasm as the honored guest or friend, because there's always one more place at the table at home.

And when the time comes in one's life to choose one's home—to really choose it—Oh! Let me tell you, they are going to hoop and holler and applaud! Not because there'll be an extra room now. Not because someone else will be picking up all those socks. Not because those silly knock-knock jokes will finally end. No, they will hoop and holler and applaud because out of all the craziness in our world that promises one's sure failure in life, relationship and all that we could ever hope to be, choosing this one place called 'home' is by far the best decision one can ever, ever make. 👑

The Regular Kingdom and the Beautiful Kingdom

*A fairy tale for all those
who have peeked over
the fence and longed
for a place called
"The Beautiful Kingdom."*

ONCE, I REALLY BELIEVED THE WORLD DIVIDED up into two kingdoms. One kingdom was regular and the other kingdom was beautiful.

The Beautiful Kingdom had green rolling hills with a huge river that ran alongside them. There were trees of every kind, crops, livestock, fields full of flowers, and beautifully planned communities with easy-access expressways, all leading to the huge downtown shopping and recreational area.

And, of course, in such a beautiful kingdom there would be beautiful people. They were gorgeous, well-educated, outstanding in manners, character and citizenship—perfect in every way. Perfectly beautiful!

The mayor was beautiful. The mayor's wife and six children were beautiful. The secretaries, store clerks, butchers, bakers and barbers, the hair designers, manicurists, facialists, plumbers, painters, preachers, and principals, the teachers, technicians, doctors, dentists, librarians, agrarians and veterinarians, the gardeners, gas station attendants, grandparents, mothers, fathers, children—even the wrinkled, pink, little newborns—all were beautiful!

The beautiful people of this kingdom knew that people from the other kingdom—The Regular Kingdom—wanted to live in their kingdom. So, you can imagine how overjoyed I was when I received permission to visit my Aunt Edith in The Beautiful Kingdom.

I am from the other kingdom—The Regular Kingdom. It's nothing like The Beautiful Kingdom. It's kind of normal, average, everyday, unpretentious, ordinary, typical, familiar, commonplace—and terribly regular in The Regular Kingdom.

As the bus drove away from the station that Saturday, the gray, average, regular-shaped buildings, the dull, flat, plain old landscape, the handful of regular well-wishers—my dad, my best friend, and my very regular little brother—got smaller and smaller as I stared out the back window until my kingdom disappeared.

I dozed off and on as we bumped along and then, after what seemed like hours, I saw it off in the distance. The Beautiful Kingdom! As the bus rolled to a stop, I could hardly take it all in. It was so much more than any description or postcard. I searched the crowd for my aunt. There—there she was! Beautiful. Cool. She hadn't changed at all. She brushed my cheek with a kiss and said those familiar words, "My, how you've grown."

I felt so odd, so ordinary, so regular among all the beauty of this kingdom. My aunt must have sensed this for she took me on an immediate shopping spree. My own new wardrobe of beautiful clothes with tags and labels that said very important things, not just "100% cotton, wash and tumble dry." I felt less regular each time we bought something.

Then we ate lunch at a real French restaurant. My plate was a picture of beauty, right down to the tomato rose and basil garnish.

Oh, how I enjoyed my first day in this kingdom! The party Aunt Edith gave me was a dream come true. Meeting all the people she knew, swimming in her Olympic-sized pool with waterfall and Jacuzzi left me breathless. And my very own room, complete with entertainment center, dressing area and bathroom, was more than I had ever imagined.

That night, as I slipped between my powder blue silk sheets, something began to change. I knew that night that I never wanted to leave this kingdom.

The next morning I was up early with my aunt's favorite breakfast set before her. Swallowing my first bite, I ventured, "Aunt Edith, I need to ask you a question."

"My dear, I already know. Who wouldn't want to live in this kingdom? However, the more important question you should be asking is this: 'What must I do to be granted citizenship to The Beautiful Kingdom?'"

The suspense was killing me. I swallowed my last bite of French toast and blurted it out.

"What? Aunt Edith, what do I have to do?"

"Change," she said in a cool, knowing tone.

"Change?"

"Yes, change. Change everything."

"Oh, okay. All right."

"Well, my dear, are you ready to work, really hard?"

"Yes!"

"Then let's go!"

She beckoned from the front door with

gold and platinum charge cards in hand. And we were off to change, rearrange, mold, manipulate and remake me. I was willing. I'd made up my mind. I'd do whatever it took to change enough for this kingdom.

The weeks of summer flew by. My aunt found this thing and that thing to change. A complete hair and color analysis had done wonders with my looks. Daily salon visits had changed every hair and nail I owned. An orthodontist was hard at work on a slight overbite. Weekly visits to the dermatologist had cleared up a blemish problem. Contacts turned my eyes a lovely shade of blue. A nutritionist had enabled me to whittle away some extra pounds. Modeling classes had improved my posture. And little plastic inserts from the podiatrist had corrected my fallen arches.

My wardrobe had expanded along with my good taste for the finer things. I joined an exclusive health spa. I joined an equestrian group. An art appreciation group. A ballet class. A theater group. And the list went on and on and on . . .

I could feel it. I could see it. It had happened. I had changed.

The end of the summer came and it was time for the all-important interview with the mayor. "A technicality," my aunt assured me. "There's nothing to worry about."

The reception area was quiet that day. Beautiful, but quiet. I sat there, nervously thumbing through magazines, checking my reflection, reviewing my first words to the mayor.

I must admit that, as I sat there, I had second thoughts. Had I really changed?

I looked different from the top of my head to the soles of my feet. But had I changed enough? I was interrupted from my doubts by a compliment from the mayor.

"Well, the apple doesn't fall far from the tree! You're just as beautiful as your Aunt Edith!"

My confidence was back. I walked like a model from a page out of Vogue straight into the mayor's office.

The minute I sat down the questions started. Question after question about this and that and that and this. I could feel the perspiration on my forehead and oh, how I wished the mayor had offered me a drink of water that day.

Finally, the mayor closed the file he'd been scribbling in and looked right at me.

"Well, my dear, I'm most pleased with the amount of change you've made. There is only one change left involving your signature."

"One more change?" I thought. "What could possibly be left?"

"Just a technicality," said the mayor. He placed the pen in my hand and moved the last page of my file in front of me to sign.

It read:

Citizenship to
The Beautiful Kingdom
and all rights and privileges
therein will be granted to
said prospective citizen,
providing the said prospective
citizen discards all family
and friendly ties with
The Regular Kingdom.

. . . providing the said citizen discards all family and friendly ties with The Regular Kingdom. I stared at the paper. "What is this? Discard my family, my friends? Everyone? What about my aunt? She hasn't discarded me."

"Is there a problem?" asked the mayor.

I stared at the paper again.

"Well?"

"I . . . I can't! I can't sign your paper!" And I shoved the file back across the desk and started running.

I ran out of that office, out of the beautiful high rise building. I ran past the stores full of beautiful clothes and beautiful things, past all the beautiful people on beautiful streets doing beautiful things—or so it had seemed.

Out of breath, confused, I burst through the door of my aunt's home.

She rushed to congratulate me and I stopped her.

"How come you never come to The Regular Kingdom? I need to know Aunt Edith. Am I your niece or am I a relationship you've thrown away in order to live here in The Beautiful Kingdom?"

She just stood there. Beautiful. Cool. Aloof.

"My, how you've grown."

The words came out of her mouth, but they sounded different.

She then brushed my cheek with a kiss and whispered in my ear words I have never forgotten to this day. "You must choose your kingdom, my dear."

I packed my things, said goodbye and headed for the bus terminal. I was going home—home to where things would be regular again.

The ride back to The Regular Kingdom was as regular as could be. There was just a hint of fall in the air, the trees were just beginning to display their colors, everything sort of seemed in harmony with itself on that old regular road—potholes and all.

Then I saw it off in the distance. The faint outline of The Regular Kingdom against the pink of the setting sun. It was like I was seeing it for the very first time. It looked . . . beautiful.

As we neared the bus station, I could see hundreds of citizens. The band from my high school was playing and a banner was stretched across the crowd. Then I saw my dad, my little brother and my best friend all waving from the front of the crowd. I looked around the crowd for the mayor, the chief of police, someone important.

Then I saw it! On the banner in huge block letters read my name and the words,

WELCOME HOME, WE LOVE YOU!

There were hugs and kisses and tears. I'd been missed—regular me!

My dad, little brother, best friend and I all

headed home to a "Glad-You're-Back-Welcome-Home" meal. Oh, no tomato rose and basil garnish on the side of my plate. But the best meal I'd eaten all summer.

It felt good to be home at last. To be with people who see you as you are and accept you—as you are.

I was home, really home . . . in The Regular Kingdom. 👑

The Fountain

An allegory.

*About a
Great Fountain
and living water
never tasted
before.*

ONCE UPON A TIME, THERE WAS A LAND AND A people who had been valued beyond compare. They had been given a Great Fountain. Right in the center of their land was a beautiful fountain out of which living water flowed. Oh, yes. It really was living water! One drink could change a person altogether.

Now, I don't think it changed a big nose to a small nose or erased unwanted pounds, but it did change people. It took away the thirsts of life. And ears that had never really heard, heard. Eyes that had never really seen, saw. And hearts that had been hardened through and through could be changed forever with one taste of that living water.

Every day, every person came for water. Some in the morning, some at noon, some in the cool of the evening. That drink seemed to make all the difference in their lives. And it was enough.

Over time though, some stopped coming. As unbelievable as this may sound, some began skipping days here and there. Some decided that they only needed the water once or twice a year, not every day. Some came only when their friends did. In fact, it became so unpopular that those few who still went for water snuck out for a quick drink after dark, when no one was watching.

And then it happened. No one came to the Great Fountain for water.

Time wore on in this land, until the Fountain became a part of history. A vague memory. The path to it became overgrown with weeds and brush. The water turned dark and still. Finally, it dried up.

And so did the people. They gradually preferred the company of dark rooms, the safety of locked doors, the comfort of barred windows. A mute-like existence took over their lives. They were alone, afraid, and oh, so very thirsty.

One of the very last things they did to erase the Fountain from their memories was to hide it. They wanted it gone.

It was quite a task, this hiding. A huge wall replaced the rolling landscape as new boundaries to the land were established. Plans were drawn, mortar poured, bricks laid, until at last, the Fountain was no longer inside their land.

One day, one hot, dusty day in August, a Healer sent by the Great King reached this land. He had been traveling a long time to get to this place. He was hungry and tired when He passed through tethered gates. Strangely, to this Man, their gates, locked doors, and barred windows were gestures of welcome, invitations to restore, cleanse, heal.

There was no outward notice taken of His presence that day, but they were watching Him from around corners, behind cracked doors, through scraps of curtains. Hoping He'd pass through one gate and out the other and leave their land.

The Healer came to what appeared to be a forgotten inn or a motel. Its rusty sign swung back and forth in the breeze.

He had been standing at the front desk ringing the bell for a while when a man poked his head through a curtained doorway a few feet away. Squinting from the change in light from one room to the next, he grumbled, "Forty dollars in advance."

The man was young but looked worn, so

worn, as if life had passed him by in some sort of
unfair way. He was careful to avoid the Healer's
eyes as he took the money and gave directions.
"Room's at the top. Check-out's at noon."

"I won't be leaving tomorrow," said the
Healer. "I'll be staying awhile."

But the man knew better. The last visitor
left before nightfall. Yet this stranger seemed different. His voice and His appearance were somehow familiar, although the man was sure he'd
never met Him before. Maybe He would stay,
thought the man, maybe. Catching himself mid-
thought, he retreated to the safety and company
of his TV.

The Healer put His things away and then
was off to find food and some answers. It was dusk
now and through the filminess of the ending day,
He saw people walking just ahead of Him. He
called out to them. No answer. They were there,
somewhere in the shadows, watching Him.

Then He saw it. A square little building
with a marquee blinking "Diner". The lights
were on, the door was open, but like the motel,
it was deserted.

"Hello. Hello, is anyone here?"

No answer. He was about to leave when a
little old lady came out of the kitchen, waving a

dirty dish towel. "Just a minute. Just a minute."

An uncontrollable cough took over her frail body. The Healer hurried to her side, steadied her with His strong arms. "Please, let me help you."

"I don't need any help. We have enough help around here." She knew the stranger had meant something else. "Sit down. I'll send out some food."

And once inside the safety of the dark kitchen, she got a good look at Him. She was still holding her arm where the Healer had touched her. His touch had gone right through her, to a place long ago in her life. It felt warm, somehow familiar.

"Get him some food!"

With that command, a young girl, wild in appearance, danced her way to the Healer's table. She stopped only long enough to place a cup and bowl in front of Him.

"What's your name?" asked the Healer.

No answer. She was totally absorbed in a crazy kind of twirling and spinning and twirling and spinning.

"You dance beautifully." Again, no response.

His eyes were fixed upon her now. "Who taught you?"

At that question she stopped. Her eyes met the Healer's eyes. She seemed calm now as she took a few cautious steps toward Him. She stamped her feet and quickly signed something with her hands.

"Please," said the Healer. "I want to understand you."

Locked in a gaze, she stamped her feet and signed something again and again and again. Suddenly, an angry howl filled the diner. "Get in here, you lazy girl! Get these dishes done!"

The wild look returned and she twirled her way back into the darkness.

The Healer ate in silence. Paid His check to an empty counter and spoke into the darkness of the kitchen. "I'll be back. Tomorrow. Goodbye."

The old woman felt her arm again. She wished the stranger had stayed longer. Did He know her time was short? How could He? He was only a stranger, with no business asking about her health.

The girl wiped the steam off the window above the sink. She could barely make out His silhouette against the night, but a part of Him had been etched into her memory. His soft, warm eyes were somehow familiar. In that moment, she'd felt a peace she'd never known before. The thought of His return made her happy. She would find a way to talk to Him tomorrow.

The Healer walked back to the inn with a weariness tugging at every step. The Great King's words made sense now. He had told Him they would be stubborn. He had told Him they would be fearful. He had told Him they would be angry and sad. The Great King had also told Him, "It will be their choice."

He wished the man peeking through the curtain, "Good night," and waited on the steps for a like response. Nothing. "Tomorrow," he whispered over and over as He plodded up the stairs. "Tomorrow," as He drifted off to sleep. "Tomorrow, I'll find it."

The morning light betrayed what the night had hidden so well. The land and buildings, which seemed empty and forgotten, weren't. Everyone knew there was a stranger now. A stranger in their land who would not leave. As He passed by their dwellings, doors clicked to lock, windows were shut and latched tight.

He was determined. He was going to find what was lost. And once He found it—well, just as the Great King had told Him, "It will be their choice."

He was thinking about that the next morning when His feet fell upon a worn path that ended just inside the walls of the land. Peering through some cracks, He saw more of the path on the other side. Something inside of Him knew this was it. He scaled the huge stone wall, leapt to the ground on the other side, and started clearing the path, trampling what He could, pulling out all the rest. Finally, He reached it. It was the Fountain.

"It must have been beautiful." His fingers traced the once intricately carved edge, now caked with dust and decay. "Beautiful."

The Healer knew exactly where He was now. He stared into the dryness of the Fountain, overwhelmed with what had been lost, neglected, unwanted. Tears rolled down the Healer's face, wetting the dusty edge of the Fountain. The tears then turned into weeping, a weeping that overcame the Healer until He collapsed over the edge of the Fountain. The sobs that shook His body turned into a wailing lament. It was as if the Healer had been wounded to the very deepest part of His being.

It was an awful sound, a wounded sound. No one in the land could ignore it. It moved through the weeds and brush. Found its way past the mortar and bricks. It crept under the locked doors and through barred windows. It went straight through the thick walls of their homes until, at last, it penetrated the very hands that covered their ears.

It was strange. The cry seemed to be calling them, by name.

One by one, the cry drew them. The worn man from the motel, the little old woman from the diner and the crazy, twirling girl. One by one, the people came.

The cry drew them outside their land. Drew them to a cleared path that had not been walked in many years. To a path that led them to a dry and empty Fountain—and a Healer.

The years of trying to forget, of trying desperately to shove it to the very farthest part of their memories, were over. Now, they knew why the Healer had come. And one by one, they made their choice.

Some fell to the ground and buried their faces. Some bowed their knees and closed their eyes. Some stared into the emptiness of the Fountain. They wanted it back. They wanted to drink from the Fountain once again.

Lost in their thoughts and tears, they hadn't noticed that the crying had subsided from the Healer and that He was now straightening up, ready to speak.

"This time," He spoke in clear, delivered syllables. "This time, taste the water." And He touched the edge of the Fountain and was gone.

Now they felt a low rumbling beneath their feet. Then water shot from the spout, soaking everyone to the bone. The water ran down into a beautiful marble fountain etched with fine silver and gold.

In only moments, the pool below the fount was filled to the top. The people stared with wonder at what had been given back. Then, helping one another to their feet, they began to give drinks of water to each other with cupped hands.

This time, they tasted the water.

It was cool, soothing, almost sweet. They had never tasted anything like it before. They let it run down their chins, then washed their faces, hands and feet. And they drank and drank and tasted and tasted and drank and tasted.

That day, they broke down the wall that stood in the way to their Fountain.

And that day, ears that had never really heard, heard. Eyes that had never really seen, saw. And hearts hardened through and through were changed, forever.

All by one taste of living water from a Great Fountain. 🜲

The Sack

A

story

about

forgiveness.

$\mathcal{T}$HERE ONCE WAS A WOMAN WHO LIVED IN A far away land. Well, actually, she lived right down the street.

She was a good woman, a nice woman, with a husband, two children, a dog, a cat and a small track home. She was always the courteous sort. Said "hi" to her neighbors, kept her garden weeded, served on the PTA every year, volunteered at the hospital on Wednesdays, held the best yard sales with all the proceeds going to a local charity. Why, she even made Kool-Aid™ in the summer when no one else's mom would make that stuff.

There was no doubt about it. She was nice. A very nice woman. But there was a secret in her life. A secret guarded and hidden and important. Her secret was a sack. A large, filthy, tattered sack.

Now, she didn't always have this sack. But over time, she found she needed something. Something for an injustice or two she had suffered. Something for the cross and unkind words tossed her way without thinking. Something for the lie she'd been told by a trusted friend. Something for the relationship that had soured years ago. For the painful childhood memories, regrets, unforgivable mistakes, her own self criticism for never measuring up. She needed something for all of that—a container, a sack.

Each night, long after her family had gone off to bed and the sounds of sleep were heard throughout the house—when all was quiet and still—the nice woman would creep down to the cellar of her home.

There among the canned peaches and green beans, the rusty bikes, old toys and dusty boxes, there it was. There, behind some baby furniture, was the sack.

Each night, in her cold, dark, musty sanctuary, she'd heave that heavy sack up on a broken down cardboard table. Then by the dim light of the cellar, the contents were revisited, almost like dear old friends. She'd pull each one out carefully, reliving the pain, the bitterness, the disappointment, the anger, the hurt, until she began to whimper and cry, anguish over it all.

Suddenly, a rapping on the cellar door would interrupt her. She knew the knock. It was the King, the Great King. And sometimes, when she heard that knock, she'd scramble upstairs back to bed. Sometimes, she'd flick out the light and pretend she wasn't there. Other times, she'd call out to Him, "Door's open. You can come in."

He'd walk right into that place. He'd step over the rusty bikes and old toys, past the shelves of canned peaches and green beans, the boxes marked "Thanksgiving," "Christmas" and "Easter."

He'd walk right over to the broken down cardboard table where she and the sack were.

He'd put His arm around her, draw her close, stroke her hair, wipe away all the tears and ask for the sack. She'd nod a "yes" to Him. And He'd sweep away all of it—the bitterness, the disappointment, the anger and hurt—off the table, into the sack and shoulder it away with Him.

There was this feeling of lightness that always followed the Great King's leaving with the sack. It was wonderful! It lasted for days and weeks, sometimes months. No more stealing down to the cellar, no more crying, no more sack.

Then she'd remember. A small something would trigger a memory about the soured relationship, the painful childhood experience, a self-doubt. And the bitterness, the disappointment, anger and hurt would rush in on her. She'd need the sack. She'd want the sack. She'd go and get the sack back from the Great King.

Again, He would knock gently, come in, wipe away the tears and take back the sack. And again, she would go and get it back from Him.

This went on for many years, until one day, she stopped leaving the cellar door unlatched for the Great King. Leaves and debris piled up around the unused door. Eventually, she learned to close her ears to the gentle rapping that continued night after night after night.

And time went by. The nice woman grew old, tired, small, frail. Her husband died, leaving her well taken care of. Her two children grew up, married and moved away. Now, someone weeded the garden, someone else held the yard sales, someone made all the Kool-Aid™ in the summer. And the sack? Oh, it was still a part of her life. Larger, filthier, more tattered and heavy, so very heavy for her.

One day last summer her daughter called to talk. The phone rang and rang and rang. Her daughter got worried, called her brother and asked him to go check on their mother. He did. He checked everywhere. He called the authorities. They checked everywhere. Never found the nice woman—just a big, old, filthy, tattered sack, propped up in an easy chair.

There once was a woman who lived in a faraway land. Well, actually, she lived right down the street. 👑

Ralph Twigger

In this first story about everyone's favorite senior citizen, Ralph finds out how good it feels to be important, needed and loved.

"WATCH AND CLOCK REPAIR . . . IF YOUR ticker's not ticking, Ralph Twigger's your ticket!" Ralph was rather proud of the signs. They were printed on a bright color with a grandfather clock, pocket watch and wrist watch at the bottom. It was his habit, on Mondays, to pick up bear claws at Dorothy's Donuts, tape up a few fliers and head back to the apartment. But this Monday when he climbed up the stairs, he saw the owner of the building inside the apartment next door to his. There was a young woman with two children in tow. "Great," Ralph winced, "I knew it was too good to last."

Ralph had had peace and quiet for two months. No one on the other side of #7. And now it looked like two small rockets complete with toys, bicycles, questions and high-pitched voices would be moving next door.

"What's that in your hand?" said a little voice, startling Ralph so that he spilled some of the orange juice he'd just carefully poured. Standing right in the middle of his living room was a little red-haired five-year-old. "What's a matter? Cat got your tongue?"

"How did you get in here?"

"The door."

"Little boy, I think your mommy's calling."

"What's your name?"

"Excuse me, but have you seen a little boy, about this tall, red hair?"

"He's right here."

"Hi Mommy. This is our neighbor. He eats bear claws too. Look at all his clocks."

Just then, two cuckoo clocks, three Westministers and a grandfather chimed the half hour. The little boy jumped up and down. "Do it again! Do it again!"

"Sweetheart, the nice man can't do it again." She turned to Ralph and added, "I'm sorry. My son's very friendly."

Ralph didn't say a word, didn't have a chance to say a word as the woman scooped up her son and headed out the door. There was no need for formal introductions at this point. Maybe she'd move in, maybe not. In the last week, he'd seen several people go in and out of the apartment next door . . . but not a family! There was only one other family in the whole building and they were downstairs. A good place for families—downstairs—not upstairs next to #7. This was going to change everything.

For two weeks Ralph wondered if #6 had been rented. Then the weekend of March 4th arrived along with a truck full of furniture, boxes, two bicycles, toys and two high-pitched voices. The racket of furniture scooting, hammering, conversation, laughter and country western music—which Ralph hated—went on for hours. He didn't get a thing done that day. There was just no way to concentrate with all that noise. About nine o'clock, though, it stopped. Ralph fell into bed exhausted and worried. This was never going to work. His clock repair business was going to suffer, those two kids would drive him crazy and this seemingly nice woman would probably have parties 'til all hours, every weekend.

Somewhere in the worry, Ralph had fallen asleep and slept soundly, past his normal wake-up time of 6:30. He stared at the clock. *It couldn't be right . . . 8:30?* He grabbed his robe and headed for the living room. Every clock said the same thing—8:30. He hadn't done this in years. He had to admit, he felt refreshed from the extra two hours. His mind remembered it was Sunday.

Blessed Sunday, indeed.

The newspaper and a cup of coffee were just what he needed. Upon opening the door he was quite surprised to find the little red-haired rocket and his older brother standing with his Sunday paper and a white bag from Dorothy's Donuts.

"See, I told ya he had a lot of clocks in there. Here!"

The two boys thrust his newspaper and a donut bag in front of Ralph. The face Ralph had made must have been one of surprise and sternness that translated into "mean." The older brother had seen that look on annoyed adults before.

"Well, uh . . . me and my little brother gotta go now."

"Yea, we gotta go now, but you can come with us if you get dressed."

"Come on Jeremy," the older one said, pulling his brother down the apartment stairway. "It's a bear claw. Hope you like that kind!" And they were gone. Ralph was left standing there with a bear claw and the Sunday paper. He was somewhat stunned. *What did this little gesture of kindness mean?* It made no sense. Neighborliness was foreign to Ralph. In fact, it was the unwritten code of the building: You mind your business, I'll mind my business. Which suited Ralph's entire existence in life. People get close, then they leave.

The day had been surprisingly uneventful. But in the afternoon, Ralph smelled something wonderful cooking next door. Something garlicky and full of onions. Pot roast. The smell wafted its way into his little study. He tried to ignore it, but it assaulted him in the nose again and again. Then another smell took up the barrage. It was *a pastry, no a pie, yes… an apple pie with just the right amount of cinnamon.*

His wife used to make these wonderful apple pies with two different kinds of apples. His stomach began to growl. "This is ridiculous!" He headed for the kitchen for a snack. In the living room, the smell was worse! Well, not worse, but overwhelmingly delicious. "This is ridiculous!" He'd said it twice. "Now, go away smell!" He stuffed some Ritz™ crackers into his mouth, washing it down with chocolate milk.

"Mr. Twigger?" His nose pressed against the screen door.

"What do you want?"

"Did you like the bear claw, Mr. Twigger?"

"Yes, thank you. How do you know my name?"

"I got one of these papers here with your apartment's number and your name. Our cuckoo clock won't cuckoo. Can you fix it Mr. Twigger?"

"Well...I don't know."

"We'll pay you a whole dinner for lookin' at it."

"Well . . . I . . . "

"We're eating at six o'clock."

"Wait . . . I don't fix clocks for dinners!"

As quickly as he'd appeared, he was gone. *Dinner?!* He didn't eat dinner with anyone, except himself. Certainly didn't want to eat with two yammering kids and their mother. Once again, the smell smacked him in the face. Yankee Pot roast and apple pie had always been favorites.

At six o'clock sharp Ralph Twigger was at the apartment door of #6 in his new sweater from his sister, bow tie, polished shoes, and shaved whiskers . . . and his little bag of tools under his arm. He looked a little like Mr. Rogers, except Mr. Rogers was a lot friendlier.

The door opened and it was like he was looking at his wife 30 years ago. Same strawberry blonde hair, freckled smile, brown eyes. He let out a little gasp and with it came her name in a whisper, "Rachel."

"No, my name's Debra. Are you okay, Mr. Twigger?"

"Excuse me. I'm fine. Just a little hungry, I guess."

"Here. You sit down right here." She handed him a small glass of tomato juice. "The boys will be right out."

He noticed the cuckoo clock laying on the coffee table. He'd always been partial to these clocks. "She's a beauty."

"It was my father's. He bought it in Germany during the war and shipped it home to Mama. When he died, it was the only thing I wanted. It hasn't kept time for years, but it hangs on the wall to remind us of Grandpa."

All the time she'd been talking, Ralph had been fidgeting with the main spring. "Let's hang her on the wall and have a look."

She already had a nail on a wall hidden among dozens of family pictures.

"Right here, Mr. Twigger."

He pulled the weights, set the pendulum to swinging, turned the hands to a minute before six and unhooked the door for the cuckoo bird. It sure was a long minute. He stared at the faces on the wall. There were a lot of smiles, and those two little rockets dominated all the happy faces. He was then caught by a high school picture of Debra. Suddenly, he was transported back to a porch swing, a warm summer evening and a first kiss. Just then a cuckoo rang through the room.

"It works! You're a genius, Mr. Twigger!" She gave his arm a little squeeze.

The boys came galloping down the hall.

"Woah, cool!"—the oldest rocket.

"The cuckoo's alive again! Yea!"—the youngest rocket.

"Mr. Twigger these are my two boys—Josh, my oldest and Jeremy my youngest. Why don't we sit down and celebrate your fine craftsmanship."

Ralph sat at the head of the table opposite Debra, flanked by Josh and Jeremy. Jeremy stuck his hand into Ralph's folded hands and began a prayer to end all prayers, thanking God for food, rocks, bugs, dessert, cuckoo clocks and his new friend, Mr. Twigger.

It was the most delicious home-cooked meal Ralph had eaten in well . . . years. He had seconds on everything, including the pie. The conversation was pretty satisfying, too. These people seemed so interested in him. He felt important. Ralph even told a few of his favorite riddles, which the boys loved. However, they sat too close on the couch next to him.

The cuckoo clock struck nine and Ralph, like Cinderella at the ball, left quickly, abruptly.

"Please, let me pay you for the repairs, Mr. Twigger."

"No" was all he could mutter upon scooping up his bag of tools.

"Goodnight Mr. Twigger," came a little voice from the bedroom.

In seconds, he was back in his apartment. All of the sudden, he realized he might have appeared rude, but it was nine and he'd stayed too long, maybe said too much, let them in too far. He didn't do this with any of his customers, certainly not any of the tenants. He felt strange about the whole evening now.

They'll expect things from me now . . . like 'hellos' and screen door repairs and cups of sugar. Oh, Rachel, why did you have to die? You were so much better at this. You'd love this girl. She looks like you. She cooks like you. And those boys. They think I'm funny, just like you ... No! I can't do it, Rachel! I don't know how to do it. I won't let them in.

The walls had always been very thin—too thin back where Ralph worked on the clocks and watches late at night. And tonight was no exception. He heard Debra's voice. It sounded like she was on the phone with her mom or somebody important. She was chattering away. He wasn't really listening, eavesdropping, until he heard his own name, "Mr. Twigger."

Well, she doesn't waste any time. Probably trying to fix me up with her mom.

Very quietly, he scooted the chair over to the wall.

"The boys loved him. He's so cute. He fixed Dad's clock and didn't charge us a thing. In fact, he reminds me of Dad."

Yup, she's on the phone to her mom.

"Bless his day tomorrow, God. Fill it with business and show us how to love him. He's going to be a good neighbor. Thank you for our new home. Thank you for our new friend, Ralph Twigger."

An unexpected tear trickled down Ralph's cheek and plopped onto his sweater sleeve. He hadn't heard someone do that for a long time. Oh, Rachel used to do it all the time, but Ralph never believed in it much. He didn't know what to make out of all of this evening. It was confusing and enjoyable and it was kind of like having Rachel around. But people these days are pretty strange. It was better to keep your distance and keep your guard up. He decided to lay low in #7 for a few days and keep his guard up.

The next morning he was up by 6:30 working for a full hour before the fuss started next door.

"I don't want to go to school."

"You have to, Jeremy. Mommy's got to go to work soon."

"No. I won't go. I don't know anyone there."

"I don't know anyone at my new job, either. But I'm going to make new friends, just like you."

"No!"

"Mom, it's 7:30!"

"Josh, you sure you'll be okay? I hate to leave you with him like this, but I've got to go . . . I'll be late!"

"We'll be okay, mom."

There was a door closing followed by heels hastily clicking down the stairway.

Ralph couldn't believe his ears. This nice mother had left two little boys to fend for themselves. *Geraldo should know about this.* Right after that it started up again.

"No way! You can't make me! You're not Mom!"

"No, but I'm you're older brother. Come on, get dressed!"

"No!"

"Yes!"

"No!"

"Yes!"

"No!"

"Yes!" Just then there was a loud crash.

It was time for an adult to step next door. Ralph knocked on #6 and two boys, one in a semi-chokehold, answered.

"Help, Mr. Twigger."

"All right, now that's enough Josh. Jeremy, uh, where are your shoes? Josh, uh, your teeth brushed?"

"Yessir."

"Uh, good. Lunches. Um, do we need to make 'em?"

"Nope. They're right here."

Josh looked at Ralph with a sudden "a-hah."

"Mom told you to check on us, didn't she?"

"Well, uh, no, not exactly."

"I'm ready, Mr. Twigger."

"Now boys, listen to me. Okay, uh, you've got a big day ahead of you. First day of school. Big day. Uh, you two gotta stick together. You've got learning to do, friends to meet and when you get home . . . I need your advice about a . . . um, a clock."

"Cool!"

Boy, that was quick thinking, thought Ralph. "Now, you both walk home together and, uh, knock on my door and come take a look at this clock."

"All right!"

"Bye, Mr. Twigger!"

They were off and Ralph shut the apartment door. He couldn't believe what he'd just done. He'd never had kids, yet he managed to stop a fight, get a kid dressed, calm the queasiness of a new school day. They'd both be back about three. Panic set it.

They'll probably need a snack and have homework to do.

He cleared off the kitchen table of papers, magazines, rubberbands, old coffee cups from days ago. He was ready for three o'clock.

Sure enough. Ten minutes after three there were two excited little boys knocking on his door. They sat down to a sumptuous snack of Ritz^{TM} crackers, peanut butter and chocolate milk, Ralph's favorite "pick-me-up." After that, they diligently worked at books, dittos and coloring assignments. He had to answer a few questions, but he'd managed to fix a pocket watch during the time in between.

"Mr. Twigger?"

Both of them were standing at his office door.

"We're done."

"Yeah, we're done, so we can help you with that clock now."

"Clock? Oh, yes, the clock I need your advice on." He pulled a large clock covered in cloth off the shelf.

"Now, this is a clock I'm making . . . "

"Cool!"

"And I need your advice about the hands for the clock." He went over to a little chest with all sorts of drawers. Carefully he laid out four sets of brass hands. The boys scrutinized each one, looked at each other, nodded, "This one."

"Interesting. That's the one I liked too. Josh and Jeremy, you have an eye for clocks."

Just then the doorbell rang.

"I'll get it!"

"No, no, no. You hold on there. It could be a stranger. I always look through the peephole first. Now, I'll lift you up there Jeremy and you tell me who you see."

"Oh, no. It's Mommy and she looks mad and . . . sad!"

"Oh, my Lordy! I forgot to leave a note."

He opened the door and two boys pounced on their mother talking 90 miles a minute about their day.

"I was worried sick when you weren't in the apartment. Josh and Jeremy, you have to leave a note. Now, come on. I'm sure Mr. Twigger has work to do. I'm so sorry for the interruption."

"Now, I asked 'em. I invited 'em here, Debra. In fact, it's better than you think. Their homework's done and they've had a light, but nutritious snack."

"What?"

"Peanut butter, Ritz™ crackers and chocolate milk."

Debra had dropped to the couch in a heap with tears streaming down her face.

"They aren't allergic to peanut butter, are they?"

"It's not that, Mr. Twigger."

"The boys said you leave at 7:30 every morning. Now, I've never had kids, but the boys and me did just fine this morning and this afternoon. If you need me, I'm available—at no charge."

The boys were about to burst from excitement. "Please, Mom? We did everything Mr.

Twigger told us to do."

"Mr. Twigger, I don't know what to say! You're an answer to my prayers."

"Oh, pish tosh, I've never been an answer to anyone's prayers, except maybe Rachel's."

"Rachel?"

"She was my wife. She looked a lot like you and she could cook like you too."

"I wish I'd known her."

"Me too. Now, how about it? Do I have a job?"

"Yes, only if you'll accept dinner in exchange for your labor."

"It's a deal!"

"Yeah! Mr. Twigger's our babysitter!" The boys were pumping his two arms like a seesaw.

"No. I'm no babysitter. I've never liked that word. I'm just Mr. Twigger, your neighbor next door."

Debra was picking up book bags and lunch-pails. "Well, neighbor, your fee will be ready in 45 minutes. How does spaghetti and meatballs sound?"

"I love spaghetti!"

"Come on boys. Let's get dinner ready for Mr. Twigger."

She was about out the door, when she turned back around and looked at him. "Mr.

Twigger, you are my answer."

The wiggling and the chatter and the excitement moved next door. Ralph stood there in the middle of his living room, surprised by the whole day. For the first time in many years, Ralph felt needed and loved and important. 'The guard' was definitely down in Ralph Twigger's life. ♔

The Land of Blues

of

A story about singing
a new song to God.
This is a musical story.
Learn the playful melody,
note its use in the story
and have fun telling it
in your own blues style.

The Land of Blues Whine

Words and Music by
C. Perry Moore

Swing feel ♩ = ca. 92

I've got the Would Haves, Should Haves, Could Haves, If On - lys Wish I

had b - lues.

*T*HERE ONCE WAS A LAND WHERE THE PEOPLE sang the same song all day. Day after day after day a most peculiar tune could be heard.

> I've got the Would Haves,
>   Should Haves,
>   Could Haves,
>   If Onlys,
>   Wish I Had Blues

It was called, you guessed it—"The Would Haves, Should Haves, Could Haves, If Onlys, Wish I Had Blues."

The song was composed of a very lonely group of notes, slow and whiny, with sort of a nasal resonance to them.

The song seemed to come from nowhere. At least no one in their land could remember who started it. You see, only a few people sang it at first. But the melody felt so satisfying and it was so easy to pick up that one started crooning it (I mean singing it) without thinking much about it. Soon everyone sang the song every day and every night.

And they became known as "The Land of Blues."

I've got the Would Haves, Should Haves, Could Haves, If Onlys, Wish I Had Blues

On Mondays, if you were listening, you could hear the notes that were sung strong and loud by children. "I would have had my homework done."

On Tuesdays, if you were listening, you could hear mothers singing it in unknown harmonies and descants. "I should have been an astronaut. I should have stayed single!"

On Wednesdays, if you were listening, fathers could be heard singing it very low and a bit off pitch. "I could have gone to bed earlier."

On Thursdays, if you were listening, you could hear hard-working people singing it, sort of like a moan. "If only it were Friday."

On Friday nights, if you were listening, you could hear teenagers singing it in crackly adolescent chorus. "I wish I'd gone out with my friends."

On Saturdays, if you were listening, you could hear singles singing it in soprano, alto, tenor and bass. "I would have gone to the party, but I didn't know a single person there."

On Sundays, if you were listening, you could hear gray-haired seniors singing it. In fact, they sounded a lot like the crackly adolescent teenagers. "I should have gone out with my friends."

No matter who sang it, it was blue. Really blue. Dark blue. Dark navy blue. Kind of a midnight blue. Boy, was it blue!

I've got the Would Haves,
            Should Haves,
            Could Haves,
            If Onlys,
            Wish I Had Blues

And every person in this land thought their Blues were darker than anyone else's Blues. Oh, not the notes, but the reason they sang The Blues. Their Blues were bluer. Their sad was sadder.

They didn't want to listen to anyone else's Blues 'cause their would haves, should haves, could haves, if onlys and wish I hads were bigger than anyone else's would haves, should haves, could haves, if onlys and wish I hads.

On some days the wailing of The Blues was so bad that people from neighboring villages could hear it. And on those days those people in those neighboring villages would stuff cotton in their ears and shut the windows and doors and stay inside. They would scream out their windows, "Be quiet!"

But, of course, the people of the Land of Blues never heard that or them.

But God did. You see, God had been listening forever—that's a lot longer than anyone else had been listening to The Blues. He loved the people from the Land of Blues so much that one day God said, out loud,

"Be quiet!"

And God said once again, "Be quiet!"

The Land of the Blues shook with the boom of His voice. Everyone thought it was an earthquake, but then they remembered that they didn't live in California. They stood there and held their breath and waited and wondered Who could talk that loud.

Just as they were about to turn blue (from holding their breath) God said in a gentle, loving voice, "It's Me."

"'Me' who?" they asked.

"Me—God."

"Oh, it's You, God!" they whined and started singing, once again . . .

I've got the Would Haves,
Should Haves,
Could Haves,
If Onlys,
Wish I Had Blues

"I said, 'Be quiet!'"

They did . . . again.

"Now, I've been listening to your song for a long time. And it's not what I created you for—The Blues. Let me teach you another song."

"What do you mean? This is the only one we know, God."

"Oh, my children, there are so many more songs to sing."

"There are?"

"Yes. Let's sing about what you have."

"What we have?"

"Have."

"Have?"

"Yes, what you have! I'll sing a line and you sing that line back to me. I think you'll like it."

Everyone in the Land of Blues looked at each other (which took a few seconds) and then said, "Okay, God. Teach us this new song."

69

I have life today.

I have breath today.

I have food today.

I have . . .

I have family.

I have friends with me.

I have songs to sing today.

I have . . .

And the people from the Land of Blues began to smile as they sang. They began to clap their hands. They began to dance and leap for joy as they sang this new song.

And then God sang, "I have you today."

And that stopped them. Stopped their dancing. Stopped their clapping. They really thought about that line. Really thought about it. And a deep feeling of wonder and gratitude chased away the very last bit of blue from their hearts. And the people from the Land of Blues (who were no longer blue) sang back to God with one big voice:

"I have You today!"

I Have

Words and Music by
C. Perry Moore

About
Telling Our
Own
Stories

ome should be the place where we tell our stories freely and with great abandon. It should be the place where our story is treasured and understood, where we live our stories intentionally, not haphazardly. The story we live out every day is the most powerful story we can tell to others. Even the chapters when we have lived in regret or sorrow take on new meaning as we understand God's prologue to those times in our lives. When we place our story in the hands of a faithful, loving Heavenly Father we hear and see a story line that is truly fantastic.

As you tell your stories aloud you will find that many of them have universal value beyond your family borders. Your story just might change someone else's perspective, bring healing, a bit of encouragement or a smile of agreement. Your true story is a powerful thing. As I tell my true story, and the true stories of others, something wondrous happens to my listeners. They lean forward a little more as they listen. They receive its message with a bit more awe and wonder. And why not? It's the truth!

Here's an example from my life:

Unexpected Grace

I PARTICIPATED IN A VERY unexpected miracle over this last year. Something I thought impossible came to be by the hand of God. I had a baby.

My first-born, Timothy Michael Brock, is adopted. We knew him through his loving birth-mom long before he ever took his first breath. We were there when he was born in 1987. On that day, we were given the most beautiful gift a person

could give another person—their very own flesh and blood. And we became a family of three.

People told us as they do many infertile couples, "You'll get pregnant now that you've adopted." And to our surprise, we did. Several years after Tim was born I became pregnant. Sadly, that baby went to be with the Father about the eighth week of my pregnancy. People told us, "You'll get pregnant again." And we did. Five years later I was pregnant once again and two babies—twins— went to the Father's arms about the tenth week of pregnancy on a cold Christmas Day.

I have missed those three children very much and have often thought of them playing in Heaven. In my imagination I can see them playing together as brother and sisters—hanging from

trees, running and giggling through the green
meadows, marching into the throne room of God
with tight little fists filled with flowers for Him.
Those thoughts have brought comfort and peace.

As the years rolled over, the sting of barren-
ness lessened and I felt like the banquet we expe-
rienced as a family of three was full. I accepted it
as the way it should be for the Brock family.

In the spring of 1999 I became pregnant
once again. My husband and I were certain we
knew the destiny of this child. We prayed and
went to a sonogram appointment on Good
Friday, the eighth week of my pregnancy. The
now dreaded sonogram appointment had come to
represent a place of bad news, for it was there that
I always heard the words, "I'm sorry. There's no
heartbeat." But to our surprise there was not only
a heartbeat but a 10 1/2-week-old baby growing
inside of me! Shaking and utterly speechless, we
left that appointment with good news and a real
due date on a calendar. We embraced the role of
participants in a soon-to-be-born miracle.

Grace Anah Brock was born October 14,
1999. She was a miracle right down to her birth
moment. The cord was wrapped around her neck
twice and she was delivered by emergency
Cesarean section. The second person to hold

Grace's little seven-pound body was our first miracle. Groggy and dopey from surgery, I saw my first miracle holding the second—and the biggest smile that has ever creased Tim's face. It was a smile I'd never seen before—the smile of a proud big brother. That moment is unforgettably etched in my memory.

"Why now, God?" has been my only question in the process of participating in this miracle. "Why not earlier in our lives, God? We're in our forties and Tim is 13 years old now!" His answer has been a question to me,"Why not now?"

As the months have passed in Grace's short little life, I have realized she could not have been born at a better time. She came at just the right time for all of us. Oh, how we needed her. She has filled this year with such joy, hope and stability during shaky, life-jarring circumstances. And her name, Grace—undeserved gift—has become the best word in the world. That all important word—Grace—is whispered, giggled, sung, shouted, cooed, oohed and ahhed every single day in our home. Oh, how we needed the sweet unexpected timing of His Grace in our lives.

That's an example of a fresh chapter in my own true story. Now, let's look at some other ways to begin looking at your own true story for its storytelling impact on others:

1. The 'Old' Quaker Questions.

My modified version of the Quaker Questions may lead you to some great personal storytelling. They are:

Where did you live between the ages of nine and 12 years?

How many brothers and sisters did you have at that time?

What was the source of warmth in your home?

What was the family car like?

When did God become more than just a word to you?

2. Think about your life as a long hallway with doors on each side.

One door is marked childhood, another teen years, another young adult years, another marriage, another parenting and another senior years. Think about one significant story that lies behind each door—or just one door. Is there a story from a part of your life that you tell often?

Sit down and write some of these stories out. Consider recording yourself telling it on video and audio tape.

3. What is my legacy?

A legacy is what would be left behind in your passing that others would most remember about your life. It is a bit sobering to consider, but well worth the exploration. Perhaps you have already lived out some stories that are worth the telling. As scary as it may be, ask someone who knows you intimately, "What do you think my legacy will be?" You may be pleasantly surprised or equally sobered by their response. And the result may become a story.

4. Collect those family albums from around the house and dig out some of your favorite photos.

See what stories come to mind as you remember the moments in those photographs. No doubt, there are some photographs that represent a memorable story worth telling. You may want to incorporate that special photograph into your storytelling. Have it enlarged at your neighborhood copy shop for easy viewing by your listeners.

Those are just a few of my thoughts on a process that can access your own true stories.

Hopefully, you're already thinking of a story or two by now. Someone needs to hear one of those stories and there's no better place for the first telling than your living room, in the place you call home!

May the story you live out today change someone.

I know it can. 👑

My Special Thank you's

Some readers care little for this section of a book as it feels like the author is gushing over a bunch of strangers. But if you could see these people the way I do, you'd want to know them too. It is with my greatest thanksgiving that I lift a part of who they are onto paper so that you can know how very much they cared for you—the reader.

My dear friend and only-ever-editor since 1991, Marcia Coppess. Her fingerprints are all over this book and my life. Her fingerprints began in a writer's group at my church. I watched in awe as this incredibly articulate woman encouraged a room full of hope-filled writers—homemakers, tired dads, teens with arms wrapped around sacred journals and willing seniors. I believed her words that night. And I have learned much from her unrelenting ability to always see a better way to craft a sentence. She understands the oral voice and storytelling very well. And her home is like something from a storybook that welcomes others to come in for a cup of coffee. But don't mind the toys. They belong to Colin Coppess!

Karen Newe has been my graphic artist and friend since 1989. I adore her work. Karen has an incredible ability to take bits of paper, pencil, ink and watercolors and translate my stories into living, visible, tangible realities. I am constantly amazed by her beauty on page and in person. She has wonderfully curly red hair and she's like me—very right-brained. Sometimes she sees the red light and sometimes she doesn't. Me too, Karen!

My friend George Baldwin, who also has been my booking coordinator since 1997. Long before George was a friend he was a pastor to me. He's been a tremendous counselor and cheerleader for Right-Side-Up Stories. He has given me opportunity after opportunity to storytell in front of unexpected groups and in unbelievable places. Even though he is a busy man with a full-time job and now wears about as many hats as Dr. Seuss' Batholomew Cubbins, he took the time to help us coordinate the book process for this second volume. Everyone should have a George Baldwin—a person who believes that your work and ministry matter to the Kingdom.

David is my faithful husband and partner in Right-Side-Up Stories. We've been married 19 years and for all of those years he has believed in my gifts. Many times when I have lost my way, he has gently pointed back to the path. He knows that story changes people. He believes that so much that I am never alone on the road as I tell stories: we travel as a family from place to place. And that's because David believes those moments will make the difference in the way we all serve God the rest of our lives because we have served together.

Timothy and Gracie are my two beautiful children. They are the most amazing miracles I have ever touched and beheld on earth. They both love story very much. Timothy has helped build the Ralph Twigger stories since their inception. And Gracie, almost a year old at this book's publishing, is my traveling companion through the week when we trek into Orange County for storytelling at a MOPS group or a local group near our home. My two children are the two best reasons for leaving this lasting legacy of story.

Perry Moore, my friend and fellow co-conspirator in story. Perry has been working with me since 1989. He writes beautiful music and underscoring for my stories and every now and then you hear his voice on a story tape. He's a music pastor with a sense of humor and a tremendous gift from God. Perry has an uncanny ability to create emotion and understanding with music. Check out "The Land of Blues."

Gary Bayer has been my faithful brother in Christ and director since 1987. Before I take a story to Marcia Coppess, my editor, Gary Bayer does this "edit thing" with me. I tell him the story out loud and he listens (usually with his eyes closed) to help me hear what you will hear. His guidance is always gentle and always absolutely right. If I could choose a favorite storyteller he would be mine!

My faithful prayer team and board (about 75 people!) that have prayed for this ministry and me since 1996. I will never know how many times they've prayed, how many times they have sacrificed a meal and fasted for me, listened to God's holy tap upon their shoulder concerning this book. They are faithful men and women and families across the United States and they believe prayer and story change people.

The list now changes to tons of names that mean the world to me as I write them here. Over the last two years, these people have shaped my life in ways that have made me a better person, writer and storyteller. I gratefully thank the Crider Family, Reneé Herman, Teresa Cox, Debby Evans, Joyce Vasquez, Bea Grushow, Prudence Dancy, Cari and Michael Beck-Taylor,

Marilyn and Todd Farley, the students and staff of Mimeistry International, Cynthia Newland, Brian Williams, Vicki Reese, Ann Marie Batesole, Margie and Dick Coffin, Jeanne Cozzens, Larry and Nancy Rench, Anne Floyd, James and Jennifer Booth-to-be, Sharon Rose, Sharon Densford, Dana Freeborn, Stephanie McCoy, Kim Messer, Susan Conner, Pastor Scott Bauer, Pastors Gary and Carolyn Abke, Pastor Jack Hamilton, Pastor Doug Anderson, Pastor Tom McDonald, Pastors Lamont and Angela Leonard, Marty McCall, Annika Buxman, the Hickman Family, the Holiday Family, the Baldwin Family, the Jernigan Family, Dr. Jick and Dr. Duarte.

Most of all, I want to thank my Heavenly Father—the Author of all of life—my true Home. Thank you for allowing me the privilege of telling stories in your Kingdom. 👑

About Melea J. Brock And Right-Side-Up Stories

MELEA J. BROCK WRITES AND TELLS STORIES for the Child inside everyone—from the swaggering youth trying desperately to convince us—and himself—that he's all grown up, to the elder in our midst whose age might cause us to expect her to have all the answers. Each of us—busy office worker, over-committed mom, distracted college student and electronic age child—has a place deep within that responds to Melea's stories and storytelling.

Trained in social work and drama, Melea began writing stories to communicate difficult truths to college students with whom she worked. Since 1982, her stories have taken her across the United States and into Canada telling to audiences that have varied from several thousand people to intimate settings in family rooms and the sides of hospital beds. Collections of Melea's original stories and folktales are available on more than half a dozen cassette tapes, as well as in her first book, "Right-Side-Up Stories For Upside-

Down People," published in 1998. Her stories have also appeared in numerous magazines.

In addition to storyteller and writer, Melea boasts of more creative form in the roles of wife and mom. Her husband, David, son Timothy and daughter, Grace, make their home in an old 1922 farmhouse in La Crescenta, California.

As always, she welcomes your response, comments and questions. Tapes and books are available through Right-Side-Up Stories. Permission for story use also can be requested at:

Melea J. Brock

Right-Side-Up Stories

260 S. Lake Avenue, PMB 185

Pasadena, CA 91101

(800) 369-9230

e-mail address: astory4u@earthlink.net

web-site: astory4u.com

The stories in this book appear on the following story tapes:

The Place Called Home, Volume 7

The Regular Kingdom and the
    Beautiful Kingdom , Volume 2

The Fountain, Volume 3

The Sack, Volume 2

Ralph Twigger, Volume 3

The Land of Blues, Volume 6